ORCHARD BOOKS
96 Leonard Street, London EC2A 4RH
Orchard Books Australia
14 Mars Road, Lane Cove, NSW 2066
First published in Great Britain 1993
Text and illustrations © Gerald Hawksley 1993
The right of Gerald Hawksley to be identified as the
author of this work has been asserted by him in accordance
with the Copyright, Designs and Patents Act, 1988.
A CIP catalogue record for this book is
available from the British Library.
1 85213 425 9
Printed in Hong Kong

At the Garage

Gerald Hawksley

ORCHARD BOOKS

Rosie is getting ready to go to work.

She washes . . .

has breakfast . . .

feeds the cat . . .

and puts on her overalls.

Rosie is a car mechanic. Now she is leaving for work on her big red motorbike.

The garage sells petrol and oil.
There is also a shop selling sweets
and car parts.

There is a car wash, too, and a workshop where cars and vans are brought to be mended.

toolbox   spanner   pliers   screwdriver

Rosie works in the workshop with Jack. Today looks like it's going to be busy.

Rosie's first job is to fix a new exhaust onto a car. She raises the car up on the hoist.

new exhaust   old exhaust

Jack has to put a new tyre on this car.

First he jacks up the front of the car.

Next he takes the wheel off and puts
on a new tyre. He fills it with air.

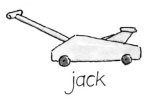
jack

tyre

wheel nuts

wheel brace

Then he puts the wheel back and tightens up the wheel nuts.

A customer has brought his sports car in to be looked at.

Just as Rosie sits down
for her sandwiches
the phone rings. A van
has broken down
in the town centre.

Rosie goes out to pick up the van in
the breakdown truck.

Rosie fixes the van onto the towing bar. She makes sure it is safe.

Then she turns on her flashing light and tows the van back to the workshop.

Back at the workshop Rosie finds that the van's engine has run out of oil and won't work.

inspection lamp

dipstick

oil

Rosie makes a start on the van. She knows Chris the carpenter needs it for his work.

Meanwhile, Jack is trying to find out the cause of the rattle in the sports car.

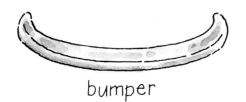
bumper

headlights

windscreen wipers

steering wheel

wing mirror

windscreen

Jack can't find anything wrong with the sports car. He asks Rosie to help.

The customer has come back for his car.
Rosie tells him what the problem was . . .

Rosie's friend, Joanna, pops in with her daughter, Annie. The chain has come off Annie's bike, but Rosie soon fixes that.

At the end of the day Rosie and Jack tidy up, put all the tools away neatly and have a good wash.

It is time to set off for home.
Rosie fills up her motorbike with petrol.

Jack turns off all the lights and locks up the workshop.

And when Rosie gets home after her long day she likes nothing better than to settle down with a good book.